Jelly and Bean get a pet.
He's a rabbit.
They call him Jet.

They let him play with
a net.
He gets stuck. Silly Jet!

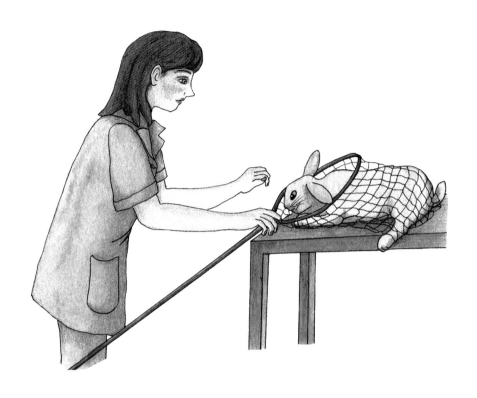

Jet goes to see Bet, the vet.
She has a look at Jet, the pet.

She gets him out of the net.

Look at Jet, the happy pet.

Jet runs away into a
hut.
But ... oh no ... the door
has shut.

The cats have lost Jet,
the pet.
They are sad and they
fret.

Jelly and Bean go to the hut.
But ... oh no ... the door is shut.

They push and push
until they get ...
into the hut to see the
pet.